The shallow seas ot Wales

Paul Kay

Introduction

There can be no disputing the fact that Wales remains a country with many beautiful, wild and remote areas – above water that is. But there is another side to the natural heritage of Wales, one which is largely unknown as it remains hidden to the majority of its population and visitors – this is the world which exists below the seas surrounding the Welsh coast.

The undersea world is a complex place. Wales has its share of the exotic and fascinating. It has Skomer Island, Britain's second Marine Nature Reserve, with its variety of south-western species, many of which are not found any further to the north around the Welsh coast. There are the legend-rich Sarnau, pebble and boulder reefs which snake seawards towards Ireland, and the Menai Strait, a fascinating channel with an extremely variable seabed and high biodiversity. There is Bardsey Island too, renowned as a tranquil location above water, but also surrounded by an exceptionally beautiful seabed, despite the fearsome currents which wash against its shores.

Today some Welsh marine sites are even considered to be of international importance.

The undersea world around Wales is spectacular and full of strange plants and creatures. It is often an eerie, twilight world, and certainly a world of almost constant motion. Perhaps surprisingly, it is also a world rich in colour, with a tremendous diversity of life, and of dramatic variation. The almost invisible seabed is as variable as is the scenery throughout Wales, or even along the Welsh coast. Just as the spectacular Pembrokeshire cliffs give way to the smooth sandy beaches of Cardigan Bay, which in turn gradually change to the low worn rocky headlands on Lleyn, so too do their adjacent seabeds alter and differ.

As a seabed, bedrock offers a solid foundation onto which many creatures are able to anchor themselves sufficiently securely to be able to withstand strong tidal currents and winter storms; the seemingly delicate seafans around Skomer fall into this category. Many submarine cliffs have their vertical rocky walls coated with

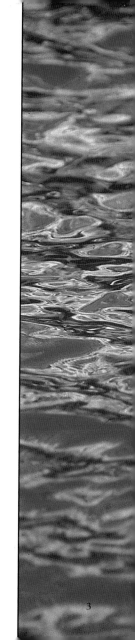

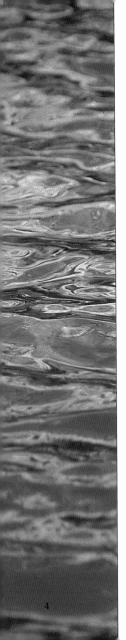

literally hundreds of different creatures, many so small that they merge together and appear as a coating which entirely covers the rock surfaces. Others, like some of the anemones, are very obvious; quite large and garish in colour. Apparently barren, desert-like, sandy seabeds, such as those in Cardigan Bay, are very different and unable to offer a firm base onto which plants or animals can grip. Despite this they too are teeming with life, much of it wary and well-hidden, buried within the sand itself.

That Wales has a rich marine heritage should be obvious from the history of fishing around the Welsh coast; an industry that has changed dramatically over the years and one which has supported many generations of coastal families. The study of Welsh seas was underway in the eighteenth century when the zoologist Thomas Pennant examined samples of seabed life obtained by dredging. In 1887 one of the first marine laboratories was set up on Puffin Island off Anglesey, although this was soon decommissioned. Today, Welsh universities still offer marine environmental courses, and the inshore seas of Wales continue to be the subject of scientific research.

It is only relatively recently, through advances in technology, that people have been able to see the undersea world for themselves using scuba diving equipment, but this still remains the preserve of the few. Whilst there is a wealth of information about the natural heritage of Wales above water and innumerable photographs which show how marvellous it is, its marine world remains poorly documented and is still rarely photographed at all.

The castle at Criccieth, which overlooks both town and sea, was built over seven hundred years ago by Edward I, and is a well-known landmark throughout Wales and far beyond. The easily and safely accessible rockpools at Moranedd to the east of the castle, which have formed as the boulder clay cliff there has been eroded by the sea, introduce the marine life of Wales to many of the children who visit them each year. (right)

Bardsey Island (Enlli) & Llŷn

Today, farming continues on Bardsey Island and its lighthouse operates to warn modern seafarers of the dangers of straying too near its rocky coasts. The island still remains home to a few hardy souls and is now owned by the Bardsey Island Trust Ltd, a registered charity. (above)

The spectacular view down the steep rocky slopes from Mynydd Mawr towards Braich y Pwll near the end of the Llŷn Penisula gives little impression of what lies beneath the waves. (right)

The Llŷn Peninsula is the extension of mainland North Wales which juts out into the Irish Sea. Its rocky coasts, in some places low and worn, in others steep and jagged, are mirrored underwater – the seabed varies from low, rocky reefs just protruding out from the sand to sheer, submarine cliffs. Bardsey, the small rocky island lying off the end of Llŷn is surrounded by rock – bedrock, boulders and cobbles – which finally give way to gravel and muddy sand at depth. The marine life of Bardsey is similar to that around much of Llŷn, but is concentrated into the smaller area around the island, with a few more species surviving in the waters here.

Bardsey is rich in history and famous as a place of pilgrimage. A lead anchor stock found on the mainland side of Bardsey Sound, presumed to have been lost by a Mediterranean vessel which was in the area, dates from around 200BC. Records are sparse and information scanty until after the 'dark ages', but it is known that in the sixth century a monastery was founded on the island by St. Cadfan, and in the centuries that followed, many monks travelled to Bardsey to escape from the troubles prevalent during those times.

In 1188 the island was visited by Giraldus Cambrensis who noted that many 'saints' had been buried on the island. Possibly, after inevitable exaggeration, this is the source of the prestigious assertion that 20,000 saints are buried on Bardsey. Wherever this claim came from, during mediaeval times it apparently led to the belief that three pilgrimages to the island were considered as the equal of one to Rome!

Visiting the island in the past was a difficult and no doubt rather unpleasant undertaking, not least because of the fierce currents that flow in the channel between it and the mainland. Standing waves and swirling waters are still disconcerting when crossing the Sound in a modern power boat. In rowed or sailing vessels the journey would undoubtedly have been frightening, especially for those unfamiliar with the sea. Given the rapidly changeable weather associated with Bardsey, passenger's fears would have been quite well founded; it could have been a dangerous passage in anything other than fine conditions.

Today, Bardsey remains a remote, quiet haven, apparently far removed from the influences of everyday life. The island has a tangible tranquillity which is hard to ignore. In spite of the difficulties, there are still those to whom island life has so

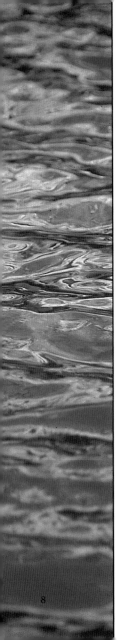

strong an attraction that they wish to live on Bardsey. Making a living here is inevitably difficult, and some income is now derived from the visitors who travel to the island to enjoy its peace and quiet, or to visit the bird observatory.

The island is still farmed, although it lacks many modern 'essentials' such as constant electricity, and water is considered unfit to drink straight from the tap. The occassional tractor may now be heard, and animals are transferred to and from the island by outboard powered boat – the days of working sailboats are long gone even here. Pleasure craft are now far more common than working vessels, with yachts from Pwllheli marina and the Abersoch moorings plying the local waters in summer. The strong tidal currents still dissuade many from entering the channel between Bardsey and the mainland, or even venturing too close to the island itself.

The fearsome currents surrounding the island have an impact on the seabed and its inhabitants, as does its location, relatively far from industrial and commercial pressures. The island has a rugged, rocky coastline. Seals can often be seen on the shore, hauled out at low tide and basking in the sun – the young pups find the rockpools much to their liking; safe to play in, and never far from mother! Below the water, rock extends downwards and this hard seabed provides homes, in many different ways, for a variety of marine creatures.

Perhaps one of the most fascinating of the animals found around Bardsey is a small anemone known by its scientific name of *Parazoanthus axinellae*. This is a colonial creature found in numerous small clumps in a few distinct areas around the island. It is somewhat unusual to find it so far north as it is near the limit of its distribution here (it is found in only a few places even further to the north), and is much more at home in the Mediterranean.

The far commoner jewel anemones (*Corynactis viridis*) are found on the submarine rocky cliffs around the island and in the Sound, but are relatively sparse, and are not found in the huge numbers associated with many similarly exposed areas. They are particularly abundant on Caswenan Rock, an underwater pinnacle to the south-west of the island, which rises up from the depths, but still remains nearly 20m below the water surface at its top.

Fanworms (Bispira volutacornis) can retract their delicate fans in an instant if disturbed. (top right)

Elephant's ear (or hide) sponge adorns many rocky surfaces around Llŷn and Bardsey. Here a tompot blenny is using part of it as a useful vantage point from which to survey the seabed. (top left)

Seal pups, like this one, take advantage of the fine rockpools on Bardsey to play in. Mother is never far away, keeping a watchful eye on her offspring from the nearby open water. (left)

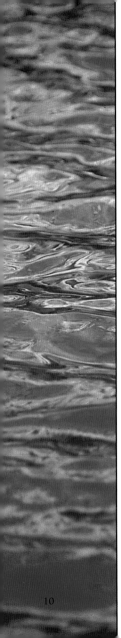

To anyone unfamiliar with temperate marine life, it may be surprising to discover that sponges are quite common in the cool waters around Britain and Ireland. Bardsey has its fair share of them. Especially abundant are the aptly named elephant's hide sponge (*Pachymatisma johnstoni*); the boring sponge (*Cliona celata*), a bright yellow species so called because it bores into limestone and shells, not because it is uninteresting; and the orange tasselled sponge (*Esperiopsis fucorum*). Many other sponges are found around Bardsey, some large, colourful and obvious, others small, drab and easily overlooked.

Kelp forests dominate the shallow rocky seabeds around the island. These fast growing plants thrive in clear waters which light can penetrate into relatively easily, and produce tough stipes (similar to thin, flexible tree trunks) topped by huge swaying leathery fronds. Seaweeds grow on the stipes, and the whole effect is of a dense jungle with a massive thick canopy. Sea urchins (*Echinus esculentus*) browse on the small seaweeds and animals which cover both kelp plants and the rocks below, whilst many fish, especially wrasse, cruise amongst them.

Bardsey Sound, to the east of the island, is a relatively deep channel. Here kelp is confined to the shallower, well illuminated water, whilst in the dimly lit depths below live creatures which fear little as they prowl around feeling for food with their long antennae. This is the home and hunting ground of the lobster. A large, old lobster (*Homarus gammarus*) is a formidable beast. With a pair of powerful pincers, one for cutting and the other for crushing, an armoured body and a secure hiding place (they use crevices and holes under boulders which they dig out and enlarge) there are few natural enemies for such animals to worry over. Smaller lobsters attract the attention of fishermen who trap them in their pots, but a big old lobster is often too big to fit through the pot's entrance, and is quite capable of living out a lifespan of fifty years or even more.

Edible sea urchins are closely related to starfish. Their bodies support many sharp protective spines between which are the suckerfeet used by the urchin to move around.
(right)

This lobster is emerging from the excavated hole it has made under a boulder. Lobsters can be considered as the underwater equivalent of a mechanical digger, and will take great care in removing pebbles and cobbles to enlarge their home. (left hand page)

The kelp beds surrounding the island are home to sea urchins which graze algae off the thick stipes. These urchins are regarded as being relatively uncommon around Bardsey, although they can, at times, be seen quite frequently. (top)

One of the most colourful fish found around Wales is the male cuckoo wrasse. The female is a drab red-brown, decorated only with black and white bars above her tail. Cuckoo wrasse are often found in and below kelp forests but will hide in suitable crevices should danger threaten. (middle)

Cracks and crevices in the rocky seabed provide ideal homes for animals like this lobster. Crayfish are now rather rare and usually only found in deeper water; they were apparently quite plentiful in the 1960s but have reportedly been over-exploited. (bottom)

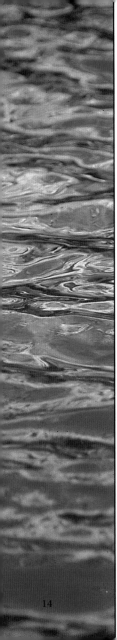

Cardigan Bay

The extensive sweep of coastline between St. Davids in the south and the end of Llŷn in the north is dominated by sandy seabeds. In some places though, are rocky reefs, or strange features like the Sarnau.

The best known of the Sarnau – narrow, winding banks of boulders, cobbles and pebbles which project out from the coast – is Sarn Badrig (or St. Patrick's Causeway), which extends for about 24 kilometres seaward, and starts just south of Harlech. Many myths and legends surround Sarn Badrig, and at low spring tides it is easy to see why, as the shallowest pebbles uncover and the seabed appears from the water, snaking outwards in a long thin line towards the horizon. It may just be that one myth – the submergence of the land of Cantre'r Gwaelod – is not purely a fanciful fairy tale after all.

Cantre'r Gwaelod was supposedly a rich and fertile kingdom stretching out from the coast between Harlech and Aberdovey. It was low lying and protected from inundation by a great dyke, the remains of which can be seen in the Sarnau.

The dyke and its floodgates were in constant need of repair and watching. One night the man charged with this responsibility became drunk, neglected his duty, and floodgates and dyke were breached by a great storm. Cantre'r Gwaelod sank beneath the waves.

Whilst obviously a legend, this tale may have its roots in the far distant past, when the sea level was lower and much of Cardigan Bay would have been dry land. As such tales were essentially from an oral tradition, they have no doubt been embellished over the years, centuries and perhaps even millennia! The current Welsh coastline has existed for only a few thousand years, and evidence of the submergence of what was once dry land can be seen at various places around the coast, when low spring tides reveal peat and tree stumps. The Sarnau are actually believed to be terminal moraines which were formed by glaciers of the last ice-age, and they may once have been features of a now submerged landscape, remembered only in terms of tales from vague mythical times.

As the tide sweeps over it, Sarn Badrig is transformed; its covering of bootlace weed floats upwards, impeding visitors' progress in a different way. This is a strange underwater scene to be found a long way offshore. (previous page)

The solenette is very similar in appearance to the common sole, but only grows to about 15 cm in length. Like many other sand dwelling animals, its colour carefully mirrors the seabed on which it lives. (top left)

This strange fish is a pipefish (Syngnathus sp.). Pipefish are related to seahorses and have a similar head. Often, they lie quietly on the seabed alongside bits of broken off seaweed, mimicking these to avoid being spotted. (bottom left)

The undersea is sometimes called "Innerspace". With strange, almost alien inhabitants like this jet-propelled little cuttlefish, the name seems very apt. Little cuttles bury themselves in the sand, but if disturbed will jet along squirting out bursts of black ink to confuse their enemies. (right)

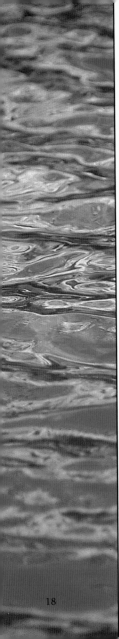

The Rhinog mountains of Snowdonia produce a
spectacular backdrop to the coast of North Cardigan Bay.
(top)

In the north of Cardigan Bay are the sands of Morfa
Harlech. These stretch northwards, backed by marram
grass covered sand dunes, and are crowned by the cloud
capped mountains of Snowdonia. (middle)

During low spring tides, the receding seawater uncovers
Sarn Badrig. Although several miles from the shore,
walking on this unique geological feature is quite possible
at such times, but difficult due to the covering of slippery
bootlace weed. (bottom)

In the relatively recent past Sarn Badrig was most certainly a serious hazard to shipping, and many wrecks lie along its length. These include the mysterious "Bronze Bell Wreck", the identity of which still eludes researchers, and which is now protected by law. Artifacts from this sailing vessel include cannons, its marble cargo and the bronze bell from which it receives its title.

On low spring tides, Sarn Badrig can sometimes be visited (by boat) and walked on, although a covering of bootlace weed (*Chorda filum*) makes the pebbles slippery and treacherous. When submerged it takes on a completely different character as, in the shallowest areas, the lengths of bootlace weed rise upwards from the pebble seabed. Many other plants, including large beds of sea oak or pod weed (*Halidrys siliquosa*) cover the pebbles in slightly deeper water.

In the thirteenth century, Edward I built Harlech castle in such a way that it could be supplied from the sea, and so survive a siege. Now the castle stands at quite a distance from the present coastline; deposition of sand has resulted in a change of course of the River Dwyryd, which in Edward's time might have swept southwards and skirted the rocky buttress on which the castle stands. Today, the north end of Cardigan Bay is apparently becoming shallower, and a significant area of land surrounding the Glaslyn estuary was reclaimed in the last century. This land is now protected by a dyke known as the "Cob" – the embankment from Porthmadog to the Ffestiniog Railway's Boston Lodge works – which drastically altered the course of the River Glaslyn thus allowing the harbour at Porthmadog to be built, and so enabling much of the area's nineteenth century prosperity to develop.

Long stretches of beautiful sandy beaches fringe Tremadog Bay – Morfa Bychan and Morfa Harlech are visited by many holiday makers each year – and it is sand which makes up much of the submerged seabed of a large part of Cardigan Bay.

Whilst all sand may appear to be superficially similar, as with many things this is not the case. The sand in Cardigan Bay varies; in some places it is coarse, but in others it is fine and almost mud-like. The actual creatures that can live in or on the sand are dictated, to some extent by its 'type'.

The submerged sand which appears to be the same in texture and consistency to that of the holiday beaches, has many inhabitants. Some are reasonably familiar such as flatfish and crabs,

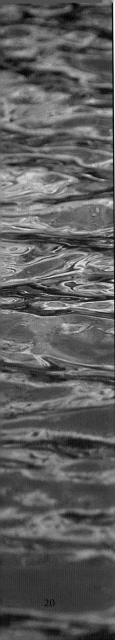

although not all of these may be the species we know best. Others are quite strange if not bizarre; one such creature is the iridescent sea mouse (*Aphrodite aculeata*), which, although the size of a small mouse and apparently covered in fur, is actually a scale worm.

Parts of Cardigan Bay have a seabed consisting of sand so fine that it resembles mud. Even here creatures are abundant. Writhing sand brittlestars (*Ophiura texturata* – a type of starfish) shuffle their way around in this murky world, whilst sea potatoes (a sea urchin) move through the surface material so slowly as to appear almost immobile.

Sand is one of the best hiding places under the sea. It is possible for animals to bury into it just about anywhere. An apparently barren seabed can become full of creatures within seconds. Swimming crabs (*Liocarcinus depurator*) can remain almost totally covered, with only their small spherical eyes protruding above the sand seabed; until disturbed that is, or when a meal is within reach. Then they can emerge at speed, perhaps using their rear-most paddle shaped legs to swim – surprisingly quickly – through the water. Equally surprising is the rapidity with which they can rebury themselves, literally

disappearing into the sand within a second or two. A slower relative is the stubbier masked crab (*Corystes cassivelaunus*). This creature is so well adapted to living a buried life that it is able to breathe by drawing a water flow down two modified "feelers" even when completely covered by sand.

Little cuttlefish (*Sepiola atlantica*) also bury themselves, but they emerge from the sand to hunt, propelling themselves around by jetting water through their bodies. These small creatures (only ~5cm long) change colour when frightened and can discharge ink in an attempt to confuse a pursuer.

Swimming Crabs are agile creatures able to bury into, or emerge from, sand within seconds. Their colouring too, helps camouflage them even if unburied. (right)

About the size and shape of a mouse, and seemingly
covered in hair, the sea mouse is actually a scale worm.
These curious creatures are sometimes to be found washed
up along the strand line after a severe storm.
(left hand page)

Masked crabs are curious little animals. They are quite
unmistakable with their long 'arms' and hunched up
appearance. Occasionally, on a low spring tide, they can
be seen at the bottom of a gently sloping sandy beach,
caught out by the greater than usual drop of the water.
The beach between Criccieth and the Black Rock is such a
place. (top left)

The seaweed sea pod, or sea oak as it is sometimes
known, covers extensive areas of the seabed formed by the
sloping sides of Sarn Badrig. It is also found in the
shallow waters off south east Llŷn. (top right)

This sandstar, a starfish which eats other starfish, lives on,
or buried in, sand. Sand dwellers, like the sandstar, may
be similar to creatures found on other seabeds, but are
adapted for, and only live on submerged sand. (right)

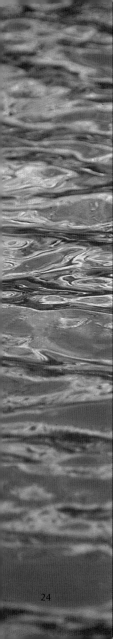

The Menai Strait

The narrow stretch of water which we know today as the Menai Strait, began forming during the last ice age. Before then, two river valleys are believed to have existed, one flowing south westwards (into the area now known as Caernarfon Bay) and the other in a north easterly direction (into what is now Conwy Bay). With the ice age came glaciers, which both deepened and effectively lengthened these valleys. They remained separated until an overflow channel formed between the two. As the sea level rose, salt water filled the entire system and the Strait formed as we know it now.

Even today, the Menai Strait can be all too easily mistaken for a river, or at least for an estuary, although its seaweed covered shores are clearly marine. The view down from the mainland hillside above Felinheli onto the area around the historic house of Plas Newydd, situated on the Anglesey side of the Strait, is one which accentuates the river-like appearance of the Strait. Here woodland flanks the narrow, fast flowing waters, and from the distance there is little visible to indicate its marine nature.

The Menai suspension
bridge is a marvellous
structure. Its man-made
beauty is reflected by
nature's hidden glories
which lie on the seabed
below its span. (left)

Shore crabs are common in
rockpools but can rarely be
seen in such vast numbers
as in the Menai Strait.
Here they can be seen in a
near 'feeding frenzy' on a
mussel bed. (right)

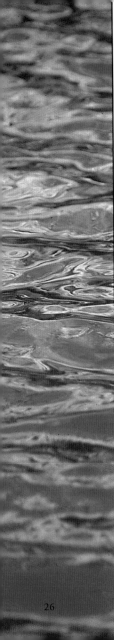

In relatively recent, historic times the Strait was (as were broad deep rivers) a hindrance to land travellers but, as a navigable sea route, a help to seafarers and traders. Now that it is spanned by two bridges and is no longer of commercial importance for merchant vessels, precisely the opposite is true.

Its current importance is as a leisure resource and an environmental asset, utilised by fishermen, watersports enthusiasts and anyone who wishes to visit it to see the historic and natural heritage surrounding and within the Strait. History is very evident; two piers jut out into it, several National Trust properties lie adjacent to it, Caernarfon Castle 'defends' its western end, Penmon lighthouse warns of dangers at its eastern approaches, and many other buildings of interest, some still used, others now in ruins, stand along its length. Underwater, the Strait is also historically interesting; it has one protected wreck, an ancient slate carrier which sank near Pwll Fanogl, and the remains of one of the last wooden warships to be built, HMS Conway (which was wrecked in the 1950s), lie scattered about the Platters Rocks to the west of the suspension bridge.

Despite the often murky appearance of the water, the Strait is actually extremely rich in marine life – over 1000 plant and animal species have already been identified within its waters. It also has a very variable seabed, ranging from hard bedrock, through boulders and cobbles to clay, sand and even mud. In many places the coverage by animals is so dense as to totally obscure the underlying seabed.

Some of the creatures found within the Strait are similar to those found off many other parts of the Welsh coast, but are different in terms of their numbers and habitat. The common shore crab (Carcinus maenas) thrives in the waters of the Strait. As its name implies it is recognised as primarily a shore dweller, but in the Strait shore crabs are abundant at all depths (it is over 20m deep in some places), and in large quantities. They can be seen eating, fighting, trying to force open mussels, and even swimming. Although they are not a true 'swimming' crab, they appear to swim in order to utilise anything being swept along by the strong current (perhaps a piece of broken off sponge) as a taxi; once aboard they can travel significant distances, before dropping off onto a different part of the seabed.

Mussels too, flourish in the Strait. Near Bangor they are commercially and very successfully farmed for valuable export markets. In other areas there are smaller, natually occurring mussel beds with many

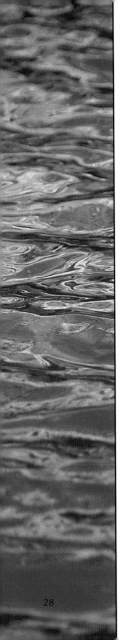

other creatures living within or alongside them; brittlestars (*Ophiothrix fragilis*), plumose anemones (*Metridium senile*), edible crabs (*Cancer pagurus*), and butterfish (*Pholis gunnellus*) to name but a few.

In the central section of the Strait and under the bridges, sponges are the dominant animals, with vast areas covered in their massive yellow, green and orange growths. The sponges too, have many other creatures living alongside and within them. Some crabs even use sponges to adorn and camouflage themselves, as does the spindly legged, scorpion spider crab (*Inachus dorsettensis*). This central area of the Strait is known as the "Swellies", and is one of the most spectacular underwater; it is also one of the best known above water, as landscape, postcard views of the suspension bridge usually include it too.

At the eastern end of the Strait lies Puffin Island. Here the rock is limestone which fissures and cracks easily, providing homes and footholds for many marine creatures underwater. This seabed is very different from the central or other sections, with distinctive dead men's fingers (*Alcyonium digitatum*) and plumose anemones covering much of this limestone bedrock.

Sponges adorn not only the Strait's seabed, but also some of its inhabitants. This scorpion spider crab purposely encourages sponges to grow on its body, presumably in order to camouflage itself. (previous page)

The undersea bedrock at Penmon and Puffin Island is covered in many creatures. The geology here means that the area is unlike other parts of the Strait's seabed in terms of underwater appearance, and the inhabiting creatures also differ. (right)

Penmon lighthouse stands in the channel between the Isle of Anglesey and Puffin Island. The relatively soft limestone found in this area provides a seabed suitable for many creatures to live on, as well as for some to live in. (left hand page)

Before mating, shore crabs are often seen 'clasped', the larger male holding onto the smaller female below. (top)

Wild mussels grow in the Strait. Near Bangor they are farmed and the area is the largest producer of mussels within Britain. (middle)

A common starfish surrounded by many of its slimmer relations – brittlestars. In some areas these are so dense that the underlying seabed is hidden from view by the writhing mass of these creatures. (bottom)

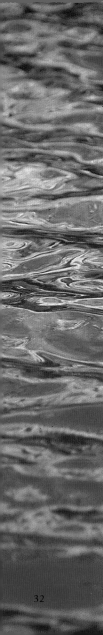

The south west and the Gower.

Whilst South Wales is rich in antiquities and pre-history, it has felt the impact of the industrial revolution to a greater extent than the North and the commercial activity which impinges on its coasts and marine environments has subsequently been greater. The rise in seawater level over the last few thousand years shaped the landscape of the south west and was responsible for the superb natural harbour of Milford Haven, and so ultimately the industry which now exists around it.

The Haven's commercial importance has changed over the years. Historically, it was used as the embarkation point for sailing to Ireland, for both peaceful and military purposes. Later it became a port and was also used as a base for various fisheries, which even included whaling operations in the southern hemisphere! Once, its exports and imports included mundane products like wool and coal as well as more luxurious items such as oysters and furs. In Napoloeonic times it was of military significance and some

men-of-war were even built here. Today, it is the oil industry which makes greatest use of the safe waters and deep berthing facilities, and a constant flow of huge tankers deliver their loads of 'black gold'.

Although there is this constant commercial activity, it does not stop marine life from colonising the waters within the Haven. Its shelter, so valuable to shipping, enables beds of Britain's only flowering submarine plant, sea grass (*Zostera marina*) to grow. Sponges like the fast flowing water within the estuary, and in places the seabed resembles, to a lesser extent, parts of the Menai Strait. Many hermit crabs (*Eupagurus sp.*) clamber around, over both sand and rock, looking for food or a new shell to house their growing bodies. Whilst few creatures can tolerate the reduced salinities which occur in the Haven's upper reaches, fish such as flounders (*Platichthys flesus*) and their smaller relatives, sand and common gobies (*Pomatoschistus sp.*), are able to and are relatively abundant.

Arches and stacks typify the coast around south Pembrokeshire. In less pleasant weather it can seem surprising that anything can live in the seething water around such coastlines. (previous page)

Sea fans are amazing colonies of anemone like animals. It seems impossible that anything so apparently delicate can survive in the seas around the Welsh coast, but many do so and large numbers are found within the Skomer Marine Nature Reserve. (top left)

The Gower is a well known holiday destination. Its unspoilt beaches, within easy reach of the city of Swansea, are popular with children and families. (top right)

Sand and common gobies are difficult to distinguish apart, especially as they both live on the same sandy seabeds and are found in estuaries. (bottom)

Further westwards are Pembrokeshire's dramatic cliffs, and offshore lie the Islands of Skockholm, Skomer (a marine nature reserve) and Ramsay. In the adjacent waters live creatures which are at the northern limits of their known distribution. Most spectacular are the large sea fans (*Eunicella verrucosa*) found around Skomer; these really would not seem out of place adorning the tropical seabeds of warmer coral seas. Here too are trumpet anemones (*Aiptasia couchi*), brown anemones with delicate blue patterning; these are animals much more common far to the south. As well as the dead men's fingers, found around the whole of Britain, the closely related red fingers (*Alcyonium glomeratum*), a southern and western species, are also found around Skomer.

Various other creatures more common in warmer seas are found in the south western waters of Wales, but are far from being the most colourful inhabitants. Temperate species include brightly coloured starfish which slowly make their way across the rocky seabeds. Vivid red, pink and white banding and numerous arms of common sunstars (*Crossaster papposus*) make them unmistakable. These beautiful creatures can grow larger than dinner plates, and have a their upper surface covered in short spikes giving them a rough feel if handled. Orange seven-armed starfish (*Luidia ciliaris*) can be seen here (they are rarely seen in North Wales), as can spiny starfish (*Marthasterias glacialis*) which can grow to over half a metre across.

The strange orange-red petal-like growths of ross coral (*Pentapora fascialis*), a hard but delicate colonial bryozoan and in spite of its name not a coral at all, can also grow to over half a metre in diameter. Masses of much smaller, brilliantly coloured jewel anemones, characteristic of very exposed rocky seabeds and clean water, are found around Skomer, but are far more abundant around the Smalls which lie still further offshore.

To the east, much of the water in the Bristol Channel is very murky; at times it almost seems to consist of thin liquefied mud. It may seem surprising that marine life can exist in such water, but strong evidence that it does, comes from the southern side of the Channel where Lundy Island is still England's only statutorily designated Marine Nature Reserve! Even as far west as the Gower it is common for the sea to be so full of suspended matter that it is virtually impossible to see anything at all below the surface.

The Gower is an area well known to the people of South Wales and far beyond for its beautiful cliffs and beaches which attract many holidaymakers and day-trippers. Sometimes the water does become clear enough for divers to see that marine life is as abundant here (and in many other parts of the Bristol Channel) as it is anywhere else.

There are some undersea creatures which evidently like the conditions around the Gower. Horseshoe worms (*Phoronis sp.*) are well known for living on limestone (which the Gower and its surrounding seabed consists of) and survive here in real abundance, together with other creatures common all around the Welsh coast, like light bulb sea squirts (*Clavelina lepadiformis*). Whilst the seabed often appears drab, it can be brightened by the vivid colours of dahlia anemones (*Urticina felina*). Quite a variety of fish inhabit the Gower's coastal waters; sea bass cruise around above the seaweed and rocks, lemon sole slide along the seabed, and tub gurnards examine the softer seabed with their sensitive feelers for anything edible.

Dahlia anemones are very common in Welsh waters, but few are probably quite as striking as this one. The dull nature of the seabed gives all the more impact to its startling colours. (right)

This photograph shows an area of seabed (which is covered in light-bulb sea-squirts and horseshoe worms), of just a few square centimetres. Many of the seas inhabitants like these are very small and difficult to pick out with the naked eye. *(left hand page)*

Few creatures can match the brilliance and exquisite patterning of this aptly named sunstar. Although so colourful, they are a true native inhabitant. *(top left)*

Although somewhat nondescript in appearance, this little trumpet anemone is a south-western species; in Wales it is living at the limit of its northern distribution. *(top right)*

Ross coral is vivid in colour and brittle in nature. Colonies of this colourful but fragile bryozoan (it is not a coral despite its name) are found in both North and South Wales. *(bottom)*

Man and the Sea.

Fewer fishing boats now operate in Welsh inshore waters than have in the past. Those that do may be specialised, as is this mussel dredger; others use sophisticated electronics in their search for fish. (above)

Milford Haven is a busy port both for commercial and leisure craft. The unseen marine life has to survive alongside industry and leisure developments. (right)

The undersea world is all too easily thought of as the last wilderness; an environment as yet relatively unspoilt by man. Unfortunately, this is far from the reality! Man has exerted his influence on the sea and seabed around Wales for many generations. Since the first vessels were built they have sunk. Their wreckage, which in places literally litters the seabed, is a continual source of fascination, and perhaps Wales has more than its fair share of the most interesting, with several wrecks covered by the Historic Wreck designation.

One of the most recent wrecks to be protected in this way is the 'Resurgam', the world's first steam powered submarine. Lost off Rhyl on the North Wales coast whilst under tow, her remains were located over 100 years later and now the remarkably intact wreck sits at an angle on the seabed. Many plumose (or ghost) anemones (*Metridium senile*) cover the hull, which is a hard oasis for a limited number of species, on an otherwise soft seabed upon which they could not survive.

Many other wrecks exist, some noteworthy, others whose position is known but whose identity has been lost over time. The 'Cambank' which lies in over 40m of water off north Anglesey, has the accolade of being the first ship to be torpedoed by a U-boat in the first world war. Some of the slaters built in Porthmadog were wrecked as they entered, or left, Cardigan Bay and all that remains of these local vessels is their cargo which, now well worn by the waves, lies scattered over the seabed where they foundered. Of later steel vessels, equally little may remain; a few pieces of plating perhaps, and only the most substantial part of such ships – their huge boilers. Wrecked ships rarely mimic the fictional word images of books – of upright and intact vessels laden with treasure – they more often resemble piles of overgrown and decaying scrap.

Fishing has had its effect, especially trawling, which ploughs up softer seabeds so that commercially important species can be caught in towed nets. Areas which have been trawled have variations in the animals living on them compared with untrawled areas, and studies on the effects of trawling are still being carried out. Potting for lobsters, if unregulated, can lead to depopulation of an area, and bylaws now control size and quantities landed.

Fisheries worldwide are facing problems, with scientists arguing that few if any fish stocks are not being over exploited. For fishermen, there is a

balance to be struck between damaging the fundamental viability of their livelihood, and catching enough fish to make a living. As with other parts of the world, Wales has its share of fisheries problems, and food from the sea is a much reduced resource, relative to its role in the economy at the turn of the century.

The results of man's worst excesses were graphically illustrated during the 'Sea Empress' disaster in early 1996, when this tanker ran aground and was holed. Pictures of oiled birds and contaminated coastlines became almost commonplace during this disaster. These served as yet another reminder of how we hold the natural world in our hands, and are able to inflict damage all too easily. A combination of weather factors meant that most of the oil lost from the 'Sea Empress' ended up being swept away from Skomer Marine Nature Reserve and its surrounding islands, and instead became deposited on tourist beaches like those of Tenby. This probably enabled the oil to be removed far better, as access to such beaches was good, whereas dealing with heavy oiling on Skomer would have been a logistical nightmare and, at best, would have been far less effective.

Whilst the 'Sea Empress' carried 'light crude' oil from the North Sea, oil deposits are now being sought from below the waters around the Welsh coast. The search for the valuable hydrocarbon deposits has been sanctioned by government, and seismic surveys and exploratory drilling are underway. Despite assurances regarding environmental safeguards, disasters such as the 'Sea Empress' episode have unfortunately highlighted the failings of the authorities to deal adequately with a problem they considered a near impossibility. With an increasing likelihood of commercially viable reserves of oil being found, the potential for further spills will inevitably rise, and with it the possibility of far more severe damage.

Welsh inshore waters are now extremely valuable (in financial terms) as a leisure asset. Large numbers of people use the sea for sailing on, power boating, canoeing, skiing, surfing, angling, scuba diving, or even swimming in! The economic benefits to coastal areas are easily seen in terms of boat yards, chandlers, charter trips, fishing equipment suppliers and so on, to say nothing of the associated cafes, restaurants, hotels and other businesses which also benefit.

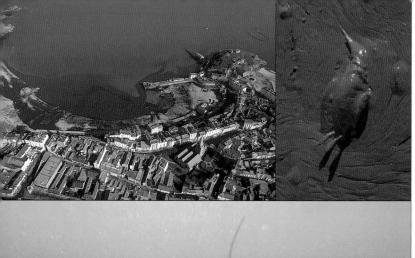

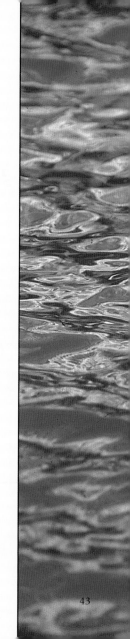

Tenby was badly hit by the oil spilt by the 'Sea Empress'. Few who saw and smelt the effects of the sea borne oil will forget the horror of this environmental disaster. (top left)

Oil is the sea bird's great enemy. However good a clean up operation is, birds still die. The only solution is prevention. (top right)

Lobster pots are successfully used to capture their valuable prey. Any undersize animals must be released so that they may breed before being taken. (left)

Visitors clearly spend money when they stay near the coast. Rockpools are still a continual source of fascination for children – and beaches are a draw just because people simply enjoy being beside the seaside! That recreational pursuits involving the sea rely on the water being clean is a self evident fact, but one which has in the past been all too often ignored. Fortunately, steps are today being taken to try to ensure that the impact of man is minimal in his effect on the marine environment.

Although public aquaria have existed since the last century, modern technology has today resulted in the ability to create exciting, new and spectacular displays. Wales has its share of aquaria, primarily directed towards providing attractions for the numerous tourists. These attractions rely on people's curiosity to discover something about the still mysterious undersea, which remains difficult to observe at firsthand. In presenting the local marine environment to their visitors, they also inevitably interpret the seas around Wales. Some provide themed displays relating to specific sites near the aquarium, others are more generalised. Either way, they offer visitors a window into the undersea, and can stimulate their desire to know more about this strange and relatively unknown world.

The natural heritage of Wales does not end on its shores, it extends offshore and should be considered to be of equal importance to that above water. It does suffer from an 'out of sight, out of mind' problem, which can all too easily result in its being considered less that its terrestrial counterpart, or even being ignored altogether. This is a pity because, like other parts of Wales, it has many beautiful and fascinating places supporting a variety of wild creatures and plants, which are no less worthy of conservation for being below the sea.

An increasing awareness of man's potential to damage the environment means that it is no longer possible to ignore an area which is merely unseen. Furthermore, the ability of the marine enivironment to survive in its present form cannot be taken for granted. Global problems could result in dramatic changes within the oceans and these in turn might drastically alter the seas around Wales. Changes in the course of warm water flows which bathe the Welsh coast could change the country's climate, so affecting us all. This means that the environment and green issues are set to become ever more important in our everyday life. Protecting our seas is no longer just to benefit the few, it is essential for us all.

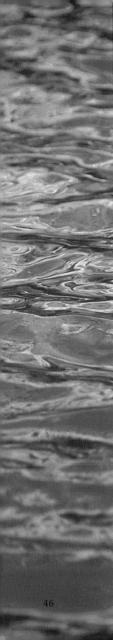

Seagrass may not look or sound very spectacular, but is important as being the only marine flowering plant, and for providing a habitat for other creatures to live in. It grows in sand and is found on suitable seabeds in both north and south Wales. *(previous page)*

The pointed nose of the submarine "Resurgam" with plumose (or ghost) anemones growing on it. *(right)*

Wrecks are rarely as they might be imagined. Here a diver examines the twisted and corroded remains of the 'Missouri', a well known wreck in Treaddur Bay, Holy Island. *(far right)*

A colourful snake pipefish (Entelurus aequoreus) peers out from the shallow seaweed near St Tudwals Islands off Llŷn. (Front cover)

The stunningly beautiful anemones Parazoanthus axinellae are found in colonial clusters on submarine seacliffs in several areas around Bardsey. This location is one of the most northerly in which they are found. (page 1)

First Impression—2000

ISBN 1 85902 854 3

Designed by MicroGraphics.

Printed in Wales by Gomer Press, Llandysul, Ceredigion